CONTENTS

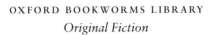

OXFORD BOOKWORMS LIBRARY
Original Fiction

Sing to Win

ANDREA SARTO

Starter (250 headwords)

Series Editor: Rachel Bladon
Founder Editors: Jennifer Bassett
and Tricia Hedge

OXFORD
UNIVERSITY PRESS

Great Clarendon Street, Oxford, OX2 6DP, United Kingdom

Oxford University Press is a department of the University of Oxford.
It furthers the University's objective of excellence in research, scholarship,
and education by publishing worldwide. Oxford is a registered trade
mark of Oxford University Press in the UK and in certain other countries

ISBN: 978 0 19 462438 1

A complete recording of this Bookworms edition of *Sing to Win* is available.

Printed in China

Word count (main text): 1,461

For more information on the Oxford Bookworms Library,
visit www.oup.com/elt/gradedreaders

ACKNOWLEDGEMENTS

Cover Image: Getty Images (young woman/Avel Shah/EyeEm).

Illustrations by: Danny@KJA artists

The publisher would like to thank the following for the permission to reproduce
photographs: 123RF pp.30 (pop singer/Natallia Charkesava), 30 (girls singing karaoke/
Dinis Tolipov); Rex Shutterstock pp.31 (talent show/Olycom SPA), 31 (television chef/
Steve Meddle); Shutterstock pp.30 (boy band/Roxana Gonzalez), 30 (choir singing/Igor
Bulgarin), 31 (television anchorwoman/withGod), 31 (cartoon vector/Danilo Sanino).

Chapter 1
The Audition

'It's your big day tomorrow, Sofia,' says Laura to her younger sister.

'I know. I can't wait! My audition for *Sing to Win*!' says Sofia.

'You're an amazing singer,' says Laura. 'The judges are going to love you! Then you can be on TV, in front of millions of people!'

Sofia laughs. 'Thanks, Laura – you only say that because you're my big sister!'

The next day, Sofia is waiting for her audition. In front of her, there is a girl with pink hair.

'Hey,' Sofia says. 'I love your hair!'

'Thanks – I like yours, too,' says the girl.

Just then, a reporter arrives. 'How are you feeling, girls?'

'Excited!' they say together. Then they laugh.

'Are you sisters?' the reporter asks.

'Er, no,' says Sofia.

'Friends?'

'Well, yes – we are now!' says the girl. 'I'm Emma,' she says to Sofia.

Soon, it is Emma's audition.

'Here's my number,' says Sofia. 'Text me after your audition.'

'OK!' Emma says.

'And good luck!'

'Thanks! You too.' Emma smiles.

Now it is Sofia's audition. The judges are watching her, and everyone is very quiet. Suddenly, she feels nervous.

'This is it,' she thinks.

She sings well, and two of the judges say 'yes.' But she needs 'yes' from all three judges, or she cannot be in *Sing to Win*.

Sofia waits nervously. After a long minute, the third judge says, 'OK, yes.'

'Wow!' says Sofia happily, and claps her hands.

Chapter 2
Friends

That night, Sofia gets a text from Emma.

> Are you going to be in Sing to Win? Emma x

> Yes! 😊 You?

> Wow! Me too!

> Amazing! Want to meet on Saturday? 1pm?
> Do you know The Happy Café?

> Yes – see you there!

It is Saturday at the café. Sofia and Emma are talking about *Sing to Win*.

'Our auditions are online now and people love us!' Emma says.

'I know! It's amazing!' Sofia says.

'You have 23,429 "likes".'

'Yes! And you have 21,632! Oh, and look at this – people want us to sing together! I like that idea. What do you think?' asks Sofia.

Emma is quiet, and she looks away. 'I don't know, Sofia. I'd like to sing on my own. I get very nervous when I sing with people.'

'That's OK. It's only an idea.'

'I'm sorry,' says Emma.

'It doesn't matter! Hey, are you going to have a sandwich?' asks Sofia.

'Yes, good idea,' says Emma, and they look at the menu.

Just then, Sofia and Emma hear a new song in the café. They look up.

'Oh, I love this song!' says Emma.

'I love it, too!' Sofia laughs.

Chapter 3
Selfish Emma

There is one month before the first round of *Sing to Win*. Sofia and Emma are doing things every day. They learn new songs and speak to reporters. But they text a lot, and meet at the weekends.

Lots of people like them. They want to see Sofia and Emma in the final.

One afternoon, Sofia is talking to some reporters.
'Why is your hair blue?' asks one reporter.
'Which singers do you like?' asks a second.

Then the reporter from the audition says, 'Are you going to sing with Emma in the first round?'

'No, I'm going to sing on my own.'

'But people want you to sing together!' says the reporter.

'Well, Emma doesn't want to,' says Sofia. 'But I'm OK with that!'

The next morning, Sofia texts Emma.

Hi. How are you?

She texts her again after breakfast.

Me again. ☺ Are we meeting today?

Emma does not answer, so Sofia texts her again in the afternoon.

You're quiet today! Nervous?

Then Emma answers.

Don't text me again.

Just then, Sofia's sister arrives home.

'Are you OK?' asks Laura.

'No,' says Sofia, and she tells her sister about the texts.

'It's because of the story,' Laura says.

'What story?' Sofia asks.

'About you and Emma. Look.'

> **'SELFISH Emma wants to sing on her own,' says Sofia.**
> Sofia wants to sing with Emma, but Emma says, 'No. I'm better than Sofia.'

'Oh no!' says Sofia. 'It isn't true. Why...?'

'Perhaps the reporter wants a good story,' says Laura.

Sofia phones Emma, but Emma does not answer.

Soon, everyone is talking about the story. People do not like Emma now.

> Sofia is right: Emma is selfish! **#SelfishEmma**
>
> Emma wants to win on her own. Bad idea!
>
> Sofia is a better singer than Emma. **#SofiaBetter**
>
> Sofia is going to win – with or without Emma.

Sofia speaks to the reporter. 'That story isn't true,' she says. 'Emma isn't selfish.'

'But now lots of people are talking about you and Emma,' he says. '"Selfish Emma" is the biggest story of *Sing to Win*! And it's good for *you*.'

'But it's wrong,' Sofia says.

'It doesn't matter,' the reporter says.

Chapter 4
The First Round

It is the first round of *Sing to Win*, but Sofia is not very excited.

'I'm going to see Emma today at *Sing to Win*,' she says to Laura. 'She isn't speaking to me, and I feel bad about the story.'

'Listen, Sofia, forget it. The reporter is wrong, not you,' says Laura.

'I know, but…' says Sofia.

'No "buts"! You need to be excited again. Do you love singing?' asks Laura.

'Well, yes…'

'Then sing. Sing to win!'

Now Sofia is on the stage. She wants to sing well, but she is very nervous. Millions of people are watching her. The judges watch and listen carefully.

She is good. The judges like her, and the audience like her, too.

'Sofia! Sofia! Sofia!' they shout.

Now Sofia feels better... but next, it is Emma.

The audience do not like Emma. 'Boo!' they shout.
Emma waits. She looks at her feet and her face is red.
Sofia feels sorry for her. 'Oh no!' she thinks.
'Shhh!' say the judges. 'Be quiet, everyone!'

Then Emma sings. Her voice is beautiful. She is
amazing! The audience are quiet now – very quiet.
When Emma finishes, they all clap and stand up. The
judges are standing up, too.

Emma smiles.

Then all the singers are on the stage together. What are the judges going to say? Everyone is waiting for them. The singers all want to be in the second round, but one person must go home. The audience clap and shout.

Then, the judges stand up and say, 'Goodbye... Harry!'

Sofia and Emma are in the second round!

Sofia finds Emma when they come off the stage.

'Oh, Emma! You're an amazing singer!'

'Thanks,' says Emma quietly.

'Emma, I'm sorry. The story isn't true – you're not selfish. Can we forget about it?' Sofia asks.

This time, Emma does not answer. She looks down.

Sofia runs away. She is crying, and she does not want Emma to see.

The next day, all the stories are about Emma. Sofia and Laura read them together.

AMAZING Emma!

Everyone loves Emma!

Emma can Sing to Win!

'I'm sorry, Sofia – nobody is talking about you now,' says Laura.

'It's OK. I'm happy for Emma, and I'm in the second round, too. But I want to be friends again,' she says.

'Give it some time,' says Laura. 'Then talk to her again.'

Chapter 5
The Final

Two days later, Sofia gets a text from Emma.

> Can we meet at The Happy Café?
> Tomorrow at 11.30? Emma x

The next day, Sofia arrives at The Happy Café at 11.30. Emma is sitting at a table near the window.

'Um… hi,' says Sofia.

'Hi,' says Emma. 'Listen, Sofia, the story isn't true – I can see that now. Reporters want a new story every day. I'm sorry.'

'Oh, thank you, Emma!'

'I need to listen to my friends, not reporters. They only want a good story.'

'You're right,' says Sofia.

There are seven more rounds of *Sing to Win*. Every week, one singer goes home; and every week, Sofia thinks, 'Is it me?' But she is good, and the audience and the judges like her. They love Emma, too. They are both in the final – and better than that, they are friends again!

It is the big final. Sofia and Emma sing song after song after song. Sometimes Sofia is better, and sometimes Emma is better. But they are both amazing! Millions of people are watching them – in the audience and on TV.

They stand on the stage together. Who is the winner? Sofia feels very nervous. They wait for the judges, but the judges talk and talk. Some people are shouting, 'Sofia!' Some are shouting, 'Emma!' There is a lot of noise.

Suddenly, the judges call the winner's name:

'EMMA!'

Sofia smiles – she is second, but she is happy for her friend.

A judge says to Emma and Sofia, 'Are you going to sing together now?'

'Yes! Yes! Sing together!' the audience shout.

Emma looks at Sofia. 'Let's do it!' she says.

'Really?' says Sofia.

'Yes,' says Emma. She takes Sofia's hand, and they sing – friends together.

amazing *(adj)* exciting and interesting

audience *(n)* the people who watch and listen to something

audition *(n)* when someone sings or dances in front of judges because they want to be in a show or competition

both *(adv)* the two; not one but the other one, too

café *(n)* You can get drinks and food in a café.

clap *(v)* to make a noise with your hands, usually because you like something

final *(n)* the last round in a competition

idea *(n)* a new thing that you think about

judge *(n)* a person who decides the winner in a competition

nervous *(adj)* afraid that something bad is going to happen; **nervously** *(adv)*

on (**my**) **own** *(adv)* without any other people

online *(adv)* on a computer or the internet

pink *(adj)* this colour

reporter *(n)* When things happen, a reporter writes or talks about them in newspapers or on the radio or television.

round *(n)* one part of a game or competition

selfish *(adj)* thinking only about yourself and not other people

shout *(v)* to speak very loudly

song *(n)* music with words

stage *(n)* the place in a theatre where the singers stand and sing

story *(n)* words by a writer about real or unreal people or things

text *(n & v)* words from one person to another person on a phone

together *(adv)* with someone

voice *(n)* the sounds when you speak or sing

win *(v)* to be the best or the first in a game or competition; **winner** *(n)*

Singers

soloist / solo artist

duet / duo

group

choir

Do you like singing?

Which singers do you like best?

Television Programmes

talent competition (Sing to Win
is a talent competition)

the news

cartoon

cookery programme

Do you watch television? When?

Which television programmes do you like best?

Sing to Win

ACTIVITIES

Think Ahead

1   Read the back cover. What are you going to read about in
    this book? Tick (✓) three things.

    1 a football game   ☐

    2 a TV competition   ☐

    3 two friends   ☐

    4 three sisters   ☐

    5 a dance competition   ☐

    6 singing   ☐

2   Look at the story title, cover, and contents page. What do
    you think is going to happen in the story? Write *Yes* or *No*.

    1 Emma's audition is going to go badly.

    2 Emma is going to be a bad friend to Sofia.

    3 Emma and Sofia are going to be in the final of the
       competition.

    4 Emma and Sofia are not going to be friends at the end of
       the story.

3   **RESEARCH** Before you read, find answers to these questions.

    1 Who is Kelly Clarkson?

    2 What is the biggest talent competition for singers in
       your country?

Chapter Check

CHAPTER 1 Choose a, b, or c.

1 Laura is Sofia's…
   a friend.   b mother.   c sister.

2 What must Sofia do at her audition?
   a sing   b write   c read

3 Who speaks to Emma and Sofia before their auditions?
   a a reporter   b a judge   c Laura

4 What is Emma going to do after her audition?
   a go to a café   b see Laura   c text Sofia

5 When Sofia is in front of the judges, how does she feel?
   a excited   b nervous   c angry

CHAPTER 2 Are the sentences true or false?

1 Sofia and Emma are happy because they are going to be in *Sing to Win*.

2 On Saturday, they meet at a café.

3 Emma wants to sing with Sofia.

4 Emma gets nervous when she sings on her own.

5 Sofia and Emma have different ideas, but they are good friends.

CHAPTER 3 Choose the correct words.

1 Before the first round, Sofia and Emma *write* / *learn*
  new songs.

2 The reporter from the audition asks Sofia questions
  about the *first round* / *final*.

3 The next day, Sofia texts Emma *three* / *four* times before
  Emma answers.

4 The reporter writes a *book* / *story* about Sofia
  and Emma.

5 Lots of people are saying, 'Emma is *selfish* / *nervous*!'

CHAPTER 4 Who says this to who?

Emma   Laura   Sofia

1 'She isn't speaking to me.'
  _____ to _____

2 'The reporter is wrong, not you.'
  _____ to _____

3 'You're an amazing singer!'
  _____ to _____

4 'Can we forget about it?'
  _____ to _____

5 'I'm in the second round, too.'
  _____ to _____

CHAPTER 5 Complete the sentences with the correct words.

audience   final   judges   rounds   singer   winner

1 There are seven more _____ of *Sing to Win*.

2 Every week, one _____ goes home.

3 The audience and the _____ like Sofia.

4 Emma and Sofia do well, and are in the _____.

5 Millions of people are watching them – in the _____ and on TV.

6 Emma is the _____, and Sofia is second.

CHAPTER 5 Put sentences a–f in the correct order.

a Emma and Sofia talk, and they are friends again.

b The judges call the winner's name.

c Emma and Sofia sing together on the stage.

d Sofia gets a text from Emma.

e Emma and Sofia sing many songs in the final.

f Emma and Sofia meet at The Happy Café.

Focus on Vocabulary

1 Write the words.

   1 You can eat and drink here.

   2 Someone who wins something, e.g. a competition.

   3 Very good, interesting.

   4 Something you sing.

   5 Someone who writes stories about people or things.

2 Correct the <u>underlined</u> words.

   1 Emma has blue <u>hair</u>. _____

   2 People want Emma and Sofia to sing together, but Emma doesn't like that <u>story</u>. _____

   3 Emma sings well – she has a beautiful <u>face</u>. _____

   4 After Emma sings in the first round, the audience all <u>laugh</u> and stand up. _____

Focus on Language

1 Write the correct words.

later   now   perhaps   ~~suddenly~~   too

It's Sofia's audition, and ___*suddenly*___, she feels nervous.

1 'Listen, Sofia, the story isn't true – I can see that
_____.'

2 The audience and the judges like Sofia, and they love
Emma, _____.

3 '_____ the reporter wants a good story,'
says Laura.

4 Two days _____, Sofia gets a text.

**2 DECODE Read this text from the story. Look at the words
1–3. Who are they talking about?**

One afternoon, Sofia is talking to some reporters.
'Why is your hair blue?' asks one reporter.
'Which singers do ¹you like? asks a second.
Then the reporter from the audition says, 'Are ²you going
to sing with Emma in the first round?'
'No, I'm going to sing on my own.'
'But people want ³you to sing together!' says the reporter.

1 a Sofia   b the first reporter

2 a Sofia   b the second reporter

3 a Sofia   b Sofia and Emma

Discussion

1 Read. What <u>underlined</u> words mean the same thing?

> **KATE** What do you think about Emma and Sofia?

> **LOUISA** ¹<u>I think</u> Sofia is the nicest because she wants to be friends. But Emma wants to win.

> **KATE** ²<u>I think so, too</u>. ³<u>For me</u>, Sofia is nicer than Emma.

> **BEN** ⁴<u>I don't think so</u>. I feel bad for Emma. She doesn't know about the reporter.

> **LOUISA** Well, I feel bad for Sofia because Emma doesn't answer her texts.

> **KATE** ⁵<u>I don't feel bad for</u> Sofia or Emma. Remember – they are in the final of *Sing to Win*!

2 Now match the other <u>underlined</u> words from exercise 1
   with a–c.

   a No, you're wrong…

   b I don't feel sorry for…

   c Yes, you're right…

3 **THINK CRITICALLY** Answer the questions.

   1 Who do you think is the nicest, Emma or Sofia?

   2 Who do you feel bad for? Why?

   3 Is Emma a good friend in the story? Why/Why not?

   4 Is Laura a good sister in the story? Why/Why not?

4 **COMMUNICATE** Discuss your answers in exercise 3 with a
   partner. Use the <u>underlined</u> words from exercise 1.

1 Read about this talent competition for singers.

A NEW TALENT COMPETITION FOR FAMILIES!

This exciting new competition is for groups of singers from one family. The three judges say 'yes' or 'no' at auditions, and after the auditions, twelve groups go into the competition.

There are three rounds, and then the final. The judges choose the songs for the singers, but the TV audience always vote. After every round, three groups go home. In the final, every singer sings something on their own. Then they sing a song in their groups.

PRIZE: £20,000!

JUDGES

| FENELLA | SIMON SMITH | JGS |

2 **Answer the questions about *Popstar Family*.**

1 What is the name of the competition?

2 What type of singers is the competition for?

3 What is different about the competition?

4 How many judges are there? Who are they?

5 How many singers are in the competition?

6 Who can vote?

7 How many singers go home after every round?

8 What is the prize for the winner?

3 COLLABORATE A television company wants to have a new talent competition for singers. You must give them some ideas. Work with your partner. Think of answers to the questions from exercise 2.

4 CREATE With your partner, make a poster for your new talent competition. It must tell people about the competition, and about the auditions. Where and when are these happening?

5 COMMUNICATE Work in groups. Talk about your posters. Then vote for the best competition.

If you liked this Bookworm, why not try...

The Big Game

STARTER
Paul Shipton

West High School boys' basketball team is the worst team in town – everyone knows that. They always lose. But that's OK – Ben and his friends love playing. Then they get a new player. Sam is good, very good. Suddenly, everything changes for the West High team, and Ben is excited. But is winning games the most important thing?

The Girl with Green Eyes

STARTER
John Escott

Greg is a porter at the Shepton Hotel in New York. When a girl with beautiful green eyes asks him for help, Greg cannot say no. The girl's name is Cassie, and she says she is an artist. She tells Greg that her stepfather has her sketchbooks, and now she wants them back.

Cassie says her stepfather is staying at Greg's hotel... so what could go wrong?